G000274131

First Mental Arithmetic 3

Answers

Ann Montague-Smith

Schofield & Sims

Teacher's notes

The format of *First Mental Arithmetic* differs from that of traditional mental arithmetic materials in that the children read the questions themselves and write down their answers. The individual books may be used flexibly and children may set their own pace. However, you might find it helpful to use one book per term.

The mathematical content of the *First Mental Arithmetic* activities should already have been covered in maths lessons and the reading content is kept simple. Nevertheless, you might consider asking a classroom assistant to work with a group of children, helping them to read the questions. Ask the assistant to note the names of children needing further help, and the activities or concepts that they find difficult. You can then provide the necessary teaching, support or additional practice.

Books 1 to 3

Each of the Year 1 books is split into two sections. If you are working through one book each term, you might aim to complete Section 1 (and possibly Check-up 1) just before the half-term break. Sections 1 and 2 are further divided into sessions. One double-page spread is provided for each session. Parts A, B and C of each session contain different question types; for further details, please see the back cover. Depending on the child's skills, a session's work may be completed during the course of a week or over whatever time span you feel is appropriate.

As children progress through the series, different levels of support are provided. In Books 1 to 3, the children have access to a horizontal number line, which is provided on every double-page spread. You may decide that the children would also benefit from using interlocking cubes or other counting equipment that helps them to work out some answers.

Encourage the children to use the following mental strategies when working through Book 3.

- For addition: counting on in ones from the larger number; they may find it helpful to keep a tally on their fingers.

- For subtraction (both 'take away' and 'difference'): counting up in ones from the smaller to the larger number; again, many children will find it helpful to keep a tally on their fingers.

Assessment

The *Check-up* tests check children's understanding.

- *Check-ups 1 and 2* cover the concepts and skills of Sections 1 and 2 respectively.

- *Check-up 3* covers all the number-based work in the book.

- *Check-up 4*, contained in the answers book only, is a photocopiable assessment covering shape, space, measures and data handling. Use it when all the other activities have been completed.

Record keeping

The photocopiable *Group record sheets* in this book allow you to note problem areas for particular children. For example, you might write *Counts objects to 12. Becomes confused beyond that.* Or, if a child still 'counts all' to add, you might write *Needs further experience in counting on in ones from the larger number.* Alternatively, you can simply record the child's marks. Use the completed sheets to plan appropriate work.

Contents

Section 1 Session 1

Session Focus
Read and write numerals to 20
Put numbers onto a number track or line
Comparing and ordering numbers

A

1 Write the missing numbers.

14 | 15 | 16 | 17 | 18

16 | 17 | 18 | 19 | 20

2 Write the missing numbers.

| 11 | 12 | 13 | 14 | 15 | 16 | 17 | 18 | 19 | 20 |

3 Write the numbers that fit.

11 | 12 | 13

15 | 16 | 17

B

4 Write how many tens there are. Write how many units there are.

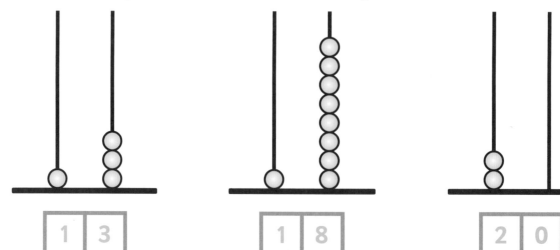

| 1 | 3 |

| 1 | 8 |

| 2 | 0 |

5 Draw lines to show where the numbers belong.

19   **16**   **14**

| 13 | | | | | | 20 |

6 Write all the missing numbers.

| 10 | 11 | 12 | 13 | 14 | 15 |

| 12 | 13 | 14 | 15 | 16 | 17 |

| 15 | 16 | 17 | 18 | 19 | 20 |

C

7 Jon has a bag of 10 toffees and 3 more toffees.
Show how many he has on this abacus.

| 1 | 3 |

8 Jim is playing a game. He moves his counter from 12 to 17.
Draw his counter on this number track.

| 12 | | | | ● | | | |

9 Write what the missing numbers might be.

| 6 | 7 | 10 | | 11 | 12 | 15 | | 14 | 15 | 20 |

8 or 9   13 or 14   16, 17, 18 or 19

0 1 2 3 4 5 6 7 8 9 10 11 12 13 14 15 16 17 18 19 20

Section 1 Session 2

Session Focus
Writing 1/10 more/less numbers
Addition by counting on
Subtraction as difference

A

1 Complete the machines.

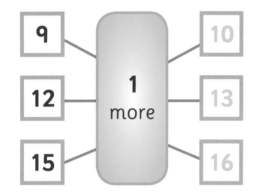

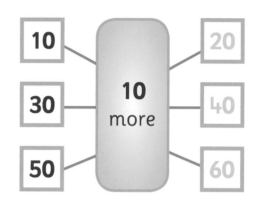

2 Start with the larger number. Count on to add. Write the total.

5 and **4** more

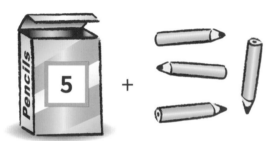

8 and **3** more

5 + 4 = 9

8 + 3 = 11

3 Find the difference by counting up from the smaller number.

 and  2

 and 2

 and  3

B

4 Write the answers.

1 more than **12** is 13

10 more than **40** is 50

1 less than **17** is 16

10 less than **30** is 20

5 Write the answers.

6 add 5 is | 11 |

9 add 4 equals | 13 |

4 and 8 is | 12 |

3 more than 5 is | 8 |

6 Write the answers.

The difference between 4 and 3 is | 1 |

The difference between 7 and 5 is | 2 |

The difference between 10 and 5 is | 5 |

C

7 Write the answer.

Amir has 18 marbles. Yousef has 1 marble less than Amir.

How many marbles does Yousef have? | 17 |

8 Write the answer.

There are 9 birds on the fence. 3 more birds come.

How many birds are there altogether? | 12 |

9 Write the answer.

Sally has 8 grapes. May has 5 grapes.

How many more grapes does Sally have than May? | 3 |

0 1 2 3 4 5 6 7 8 9 10 11 12 13 14 15 16 17 18 19 20

Section 1 Session 3

Session Focus
Subtraction as difference
Subtraction of one-digit from a two-digit number
Totals of 10

A

1 Find the difference.

| 7 | 4 | 3 |
| 9 | 7 | 2 |

2 Write the change.

20p   5p   15p

20p   3p   17p

20p   7p   13p

3 Join pairs to make a total of 10.

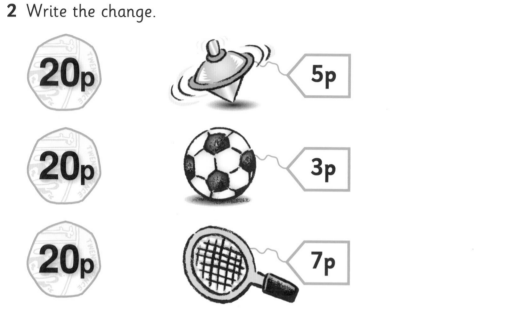

6   9   3   8   5   0

1   2   5   4   10   7

B

4 Write the answers.

What is the difference between **6** and **4**?   2

What is the difference between **5** and **7**?   2

What is the difference between **9** and **4**?   5

5 Use a 20p coin each time. Write the answers.

I spend **7p**. What is my change? | 13 p

I spend **9p**. What is my change? | 11 p

I spend **4p**. How much change do I get? | 16 p

---

6 Write the missing numbers.

4 and **6** make | 10 | | 3 | and **7** is **10**

9 and | 1 | is **10**   **5** add | 5 | equals **10**

C

7 Write the answer.

Penny has **8p**. Susie has **3p**.

How much more money has Penny than Susie? | 5 p

---

8 Write the answer.

I have **20p**. I buy a comic for **6p**.

How much change do I get? | 14 p

---

9 Write the answer.

Tom has **4p**. Bill has **6p**.

How much money do they have in total? | 10 p

0 1 2 3 4 5 6 7 8 9 10 11 12 13 14 15 16 17 18 19 20

Section 1 Session 4

Session Focus
Addition and subtraction to 5
Doubles of all numbers to 10
Subtraction as difference

A

1 Join pairs that total 5.

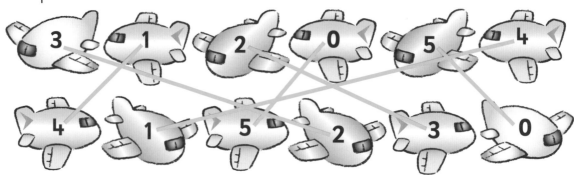

2 Write the answers.

 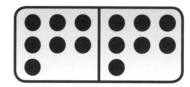 

6 + 6 = 12 **7 + 7 =** 14 **8 + 8 =** 16

3 Write the differences.

6 − 4 = 2 **10 − 3 =** 7 **12 − 8 =** 4

B

4 Write the answers.

2 add 3 is 5 **5 subtract 3 is** 2 **1 add 3 equals** 4

The difference between **4** and **2** is 2

5 Write the answers.

Double **4** is $\boxed{8}$ Double **5** is $\boxed{10}$ **6** and **6** is $\boxed{12}$

6 Write the answers.

The difference between **6** and **4** is $\boxed{2}$

The difference between **8** and **5** is $\boxed{3}$

The difference between **12** and **2** is $\boxed{10}$

C

7 Write the answer.

Jane has **4** sweets. She eats **2** sweets.

How many sweets does Jane have left? $\boxed{2}$

8 Write the answer.

Dad throws a dart. It lands on double **7**.

What is Dad's score? $\boxed{14}$

9 Write the answer.

Sam has **9** marbles. Sue has **7** marbles.

How many more marbles does Sam have than Sue? $\boxed{2}$

```
0  1  2  3  4  5  6  7  8  9  10  11  12  13  14  15  16  17  18  19  20
```

Section 1 Session 5

Session Focus
Symmetry
Sorting onto simple Carroll diagrams
Subtraction of one-digit from a two-digit number

A **1** Tick the picture that belongs in the shaded box.

   ✓

2 Write the numbers into the space where they belong.

1   2   3   4   5   6   7   8   9   10

Odd	Not odd
1 3 5 7 9	2 4 6 8 10

3 Write the answer.

12 – 9 = 3   19 – 7 = 12   18 – 9 = 9

B **4** Draw the other half of the picture.

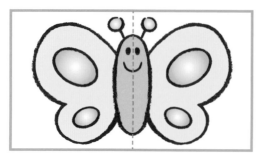

5 Look at this Carroll diagram. Join the correct words to the heading boxes.

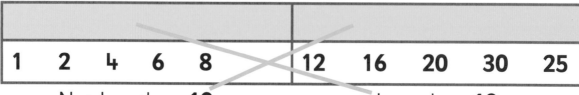

1 2 4 6 8	12 16 20 30 25

Not less than **10**   Less than **10**

6 Write the answers.

The difference between **16** and **4** is $\boxed{12}$

17 take away **3** is $\boxed{14}$ **20** take away **8** is $\boxed{12}$

C

7 Finish the picture.

8 Write the numbers into the Carroll diagram.

15   **21**   **30**   **26**   **19**   **40**   **20**   **18**

In the count of **10s**	Not in the count of **10s**
30 40 20	15 21 26 19 18

9 Write the answer.

Sam has **14p**. He pays **8p** for a comic.

How much money does he have left? $\boxed{6\text{p}}$

| 0 | 1 | 2 | 3 | 4 | 5 | 6 | 7 | 8 | 9 | 10 | 11 | 12 | 13 | 14 | 15 | 16 | 17 | 18 | 19 | 20 |

Section 1 Check-up 1

1

1 Write the missing numbers.

8 9 10 11 12 13 14 15

2 Join the numbers to their place on the number line.

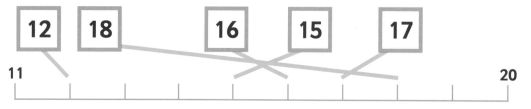

12   18   16   15   17

11   20

3 Write the number that fits between these.

16 17 18

4 Write the missing numbers.

10 less   **10** more

9   19   29

30   40   50

5 Write the answer.

Tom has **8** marbles. Sam has **11** marbles.

How many fewer marbles than Sam does Tom have?

3

14

6 Join numbers that total 10.

| 1 | 2 | 3 | 4 | 5 | 6 | 7 | 8 | 9 |

| 2 | 4 | 9 | 8 | 3 | 6 | 5 | 1 | 7 |

7 Write the answers.

$4 - 1 =$ 3 $2 + 3 =$ 5 $5 - 3 =$ 2

8 Write the answers.

Double **6** is 12 $7 + 7 =$ 14

9 Draw the rest of the picture.

10 Write the numbers onto the Carroll diagram.

15   21   30   16   18   31

Has a **1** in its tens	Does not have a **1** in its tens
15 16 18	21 30 31

| 0 | 1 | 2 | 3 | 4 | 5 | 6 | 7 | 8 | 9 | 10 | 11 | 12 | 13 | 14 | 15 | 16 | 17 | 18 | 19 | 20 |

Session Focus
Measuring length
Doubles of numbers to 10
Addition and subtraction

A

1 How long is the ribbon?

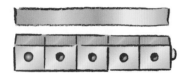

5 blocks

2 Write the double answer.

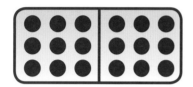

$9 + 9 =$ 18

3 Write the answers.

 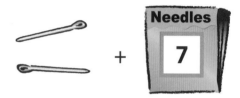

$6 + 3 =$ 9 $2 + 7 =$ 9

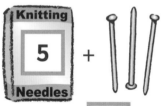 

$5 + 3 =$ 8 $7 + 1 =$ 8

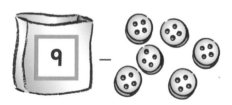 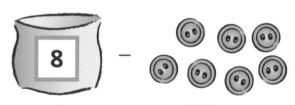

$9 - 6 =$ 3 $8 - 7 =$ 1

B

4 Write the answers.

Double **5** is 10   Double **3** is 6   Double **8** is 16

5 Write the answer.

The ribbon is **10** sticks long.

How long would **2** ribbons be? `20` sticks

6 Write the answers.

6 add **5** equals `11`   **11** take away **3** is `8`

9 add **4** equals `13`   **12** subtract **2** leaves `10`

The difference between **9** and **3** is `6`

C

7 Write the answer.

The string is **6** metres long. John cuts off **4** metres of string.

How much string is left? `2` metres

8 Write the answer.

Pat has **£7**. Her dad gives her another **£7**.

How much money does Pat have now? `£14`

9 Write the answer.

There are **16** flowers in the vase. Sally takes out **5** flowers.

How many flowers are left in the vase? `11`

```
0   1   2   3   4   5   6   7   8   9   10  11  12  13  14  15  16  17  18  19  20
```

Section 2   Session 2

Session Focus
Counting in 1s, 2s, 5s and 10s
Combining groups of 2, 5 or 10
Sharing into equal groups

 A

1 Write the missing numbers.

9 10 11 12 13 14

0 2 4 6 8 10

2 Write the total.

= 15

3 Share the flowers between the vases.

Write how many flowers there are in each vase. 4

 B

4 Write the missing numbers.

| 10 | 15 | 20 | 25 | 30 | 35 |

| 0 | 10 | 20 | 30 | 40 | 50 |

5 Write the answers.

2 and **2** and **2** and **2** is $\boxed{8}$ **5** and **5** and **5** is $\boxed{15}$

6 Use the pictures to help you.

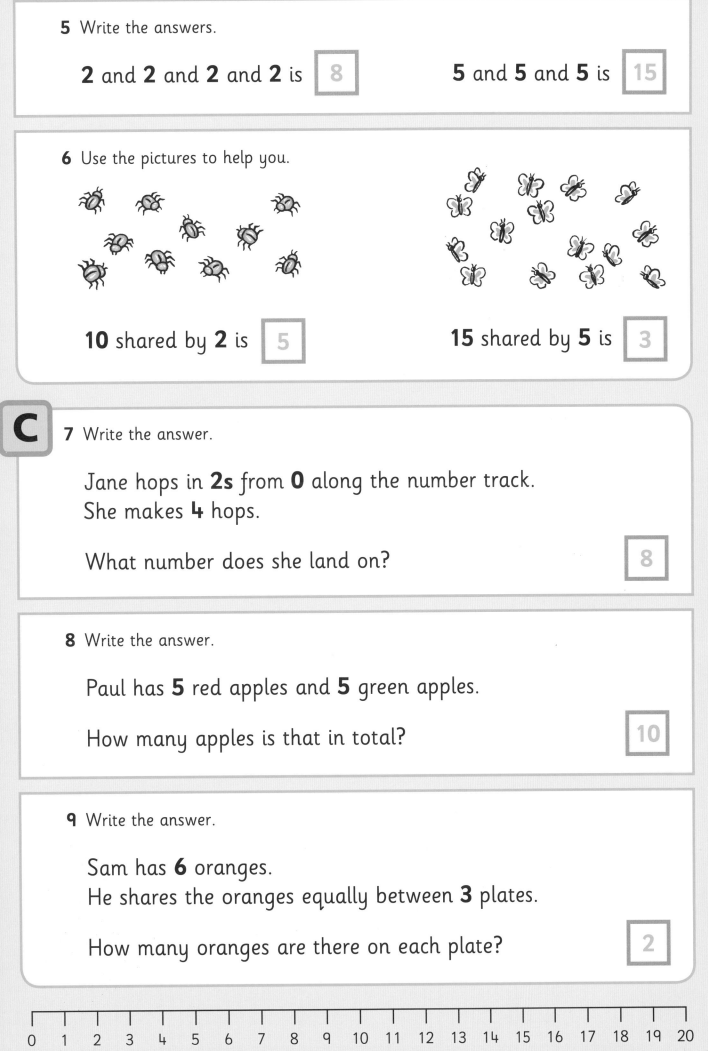

10 shared by **2** is $\boxed{5}$ **15** shared by **5** is $\boxed{3}$

C

7 Write the answer.

Jane hops in **2s** from **0** along the number track.
She makes **4** hops.

What number does she land on? $\boxed{8}$

8 Write the answer.

Paul has **5** red apples and **5** green apples.

How many apples is that in total? $\boxed{10}$

9 Write the answer.

Sam has **6** oranges.
He shares the oranges equally between **3** plates.

How many oranges are there on each plate? $\boxed{2}$

```
0  1  2  3  4  5  6  7  8  9  10  11  12  13  14  15  16  17  18  19  20
```

Session Focus
Telling the time to the hour and half hour
Addition and subtraction
Subtraction of one-digit from a two-digit number

A

1 Tick the clocks that show half past times.

  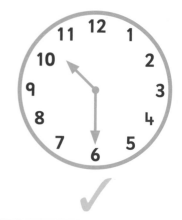

2 Write the answers.

 +     −

6 + 7 = 13   **9 − 6 =** 3

3 Write the answers.

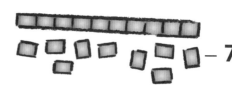

− 5 = 11   − 7 = 12

B

4 Draw the hands to show the time.

6.00   **1.30**   **9.30**

5 Write the answers.

8 add **2** equals $\boxed{10}$ **10** subtract **4** leaves $\boxed{6}$

The difference between **9** and **5** is $\boxed{4}$

6 Write the answers.

19 subtract **7** is $\boxed{12}$ **15** take away **3** leaves $\boxed{12}$

18 minus **6** equals $\boxed{12}$ **13** subtract **4** leaves $\boxed{9}$

C

7 Write the answer.

Mum leaves home at **3** o'clock.
She gets to the shops at **4** o'clock.

How long does it take her to get to the shops? $\boxed{1}$ hour

8 Write the answer.

Kris has **£9**. His dad gives him another **£3**.

How much money does Kris have now? $\boxed{£12}$

9 Write the answer.

There are **15** birds on the roof. **4** birds fly away.

How many birds are left on the roof? $\boxed{11}$

```
0   1   2   3   4   5   6   7   8   9   10  11  12  13  14  15  16  17  18  19  20
```

Section 2   Session 4

Session Focus
Position, direction and movement
Addition and subtraction
Subtraction of one-digit from a two-digit number

A **1** Tick things that turn.

 ✓   ✓

2 Write the answers.

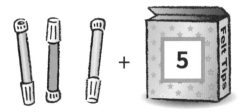   

$3 + 5 = \boxed{8}$ $9 - 7 = \boxed{2}$

3 Write the answers.

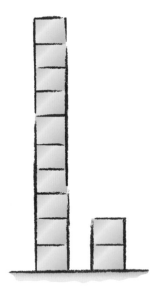   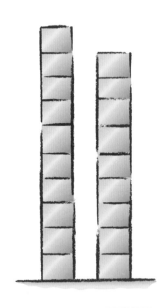   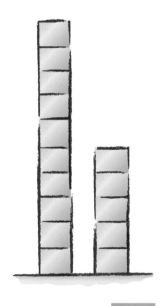

$12 - 2 = \boxed{10}$ $19 - 8 = \boxed{11}$ $15 - 3 = \boxed{12}$

B **4** Write the answers.

7 add **4** equals $\boxed{11}$ **9** and **2** is $\boxed{11}$

7 take away **3** is $\boxed{4}$ **8** minus **3** is $\boxed{5}$

5 Tick, circle or cross the answer.

Put a tick on the right side of the picture.

Put a cross underneath the table.

Put a circle above the chair.

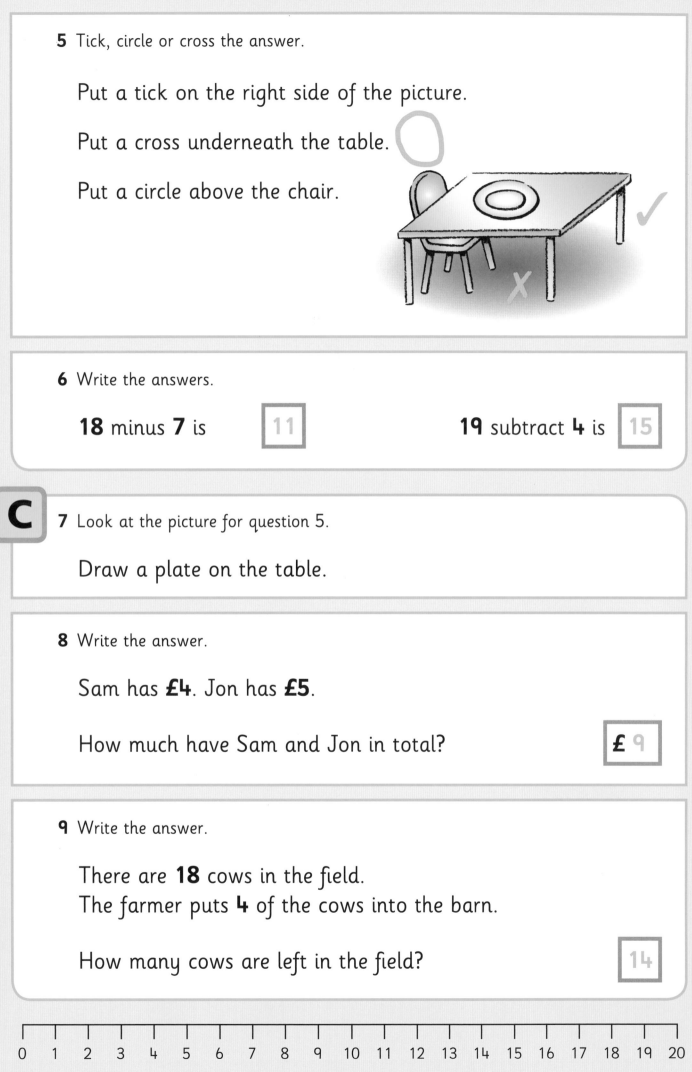

6 Write the answers.

18 minus **7** is   11

19 subtract **4** is   15

C

7 Look at the picture for question 5.

Draw a plate on the table.

8 Write the answer.

Sam has **£4**. Jon has **£5**.

How much have Sam and Jon in total?   £ 9

9 Write the answer.

There are **18** cows in the field.
The farmer puts **4** of the cows into the barn.

How many cows are left in the field?   14

0 1 2 3 4 5 6 7 8 9 10 11 12 13 14 15 16 17 18 19 20

23

Section 2 Session 5

Session Focus
Halves and quarters
Turning
Addition and subtraction

1 Draw a line on these shapes to cut them in half.

 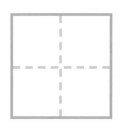 

Now draw another line on the square to make quarters.

2 Put a tick on the right hand side of the picture.

3 Write how much the coins total.

 and $\boxed{2p}$ and $\boxed{3p}$

 and $\boxed{4p}$ $\boxed{6p}$

5 Put a tick on the left hand side of the picture.

6 Write the answers.

9 add **3** equals [12]   **9** subtract **4** leaves [5]

C

7 Write the answer.

What is one half of **10**?   [5]

8 Draw along a path to the house.
Do this **2** more times.
Put a tick by a right turn.
Circle a left turn.

9 Write the answer.

Tom has **10p**. He spends **4p**.

How much change does he get?   [6p]

0 1 2 3 4 5 6 7 8 9 10 11 12 13 14 15 16 17 18 19 20

Section 2 Session 6

Session Focus
Combining groups of 2, 5 or 10
Sharing into equal groups
Addition and subtraction

A

1 Count the flowers. Write how many.

 4

 10

 20

2 Share the flowers into the vases. Write how many there are in each vase.

 2

 2

3 Write the answers.

 +  = 9

 +  = 8

 − 4 = 4

 − 1 = 8

B

4 Write the answers.

$2 + 2 + 2 + 2 =$ 8 $10 + 10 + 10 + 10 =$ 40

26

5 Use the picture to help you.

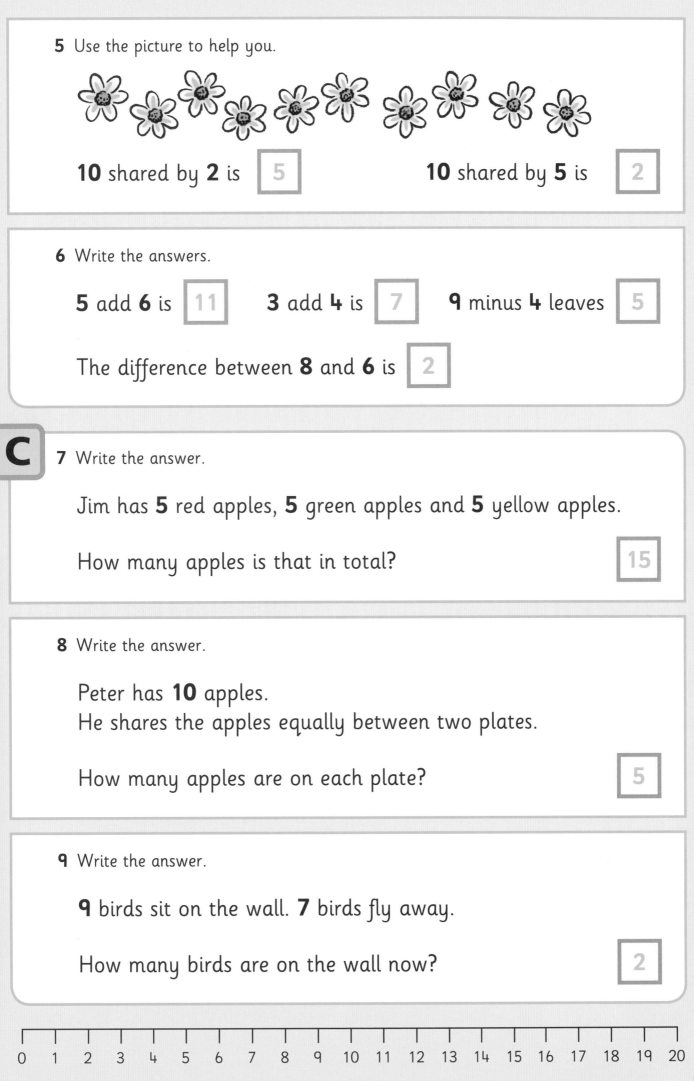

10 shared by **2** is 5

10 shared by **5** is 2

6 Write the answers.

5 add **6** is 11   **3** add **4** is 7   **9** minus **4** leaves 5

The difference between **8** and **6** is 2

C

7 Write the answer.

Jim has **5** red apples, **5** green apples and **5** yellow apples.

How many apples is that in total? 15

8 Write the answer.

Peter has **10** apples.
He shares the apples equally between two plates.

How many apples are on each plate? 5

9 Write the answer.

9 birds sit on the wall. **7** birds fly away.

How many birds are on the wall now? 2

| 0 | 1 | 2 | 3 | 4 | 5 | 6 | 7 | 8 | 9 | 10 | 11 | 12 | 13 | 14 | 15 | 16 | 17 | 18 | 19 | 20 |

Section 2 Check-up 2

Session Focus
Addition and subtraction, Ordering numbers,
Sharing into equal groups, Halves and quarters,
Telling the time to the hour and half hour, Turning

2

1 Write the answer.

$9 + 9 =$ 18

2 Write the answer.

$3 + 6 =$ 9

3 Write the missing numbers.

| 10 | 12 | 14 | 16 | 18 | 20 |

4 Write the answer.

$2 + 2 + 2 + 2 + 2 + 2 =$ 12

5 Share the cakes onto the plates. Write how many cakes there on each plate.

6 Write the answer.

$16 - 5 =$ 11

7 Write the answers.

Half of **6** is 3

Quarter of **8** is 2

8 Write the answer.

Peter's castle is **10** bricks high.
Paul's castle is **7** bricks high.

How much taller is Peter's castle
than Paul's castle?

| 3 | bricks

9 Draw the hands on the clocks.

7 o'clock

Half past **1**

2 o'clock

Half past **5**

10 Tick the one that turns.

0 1 2 3 4 5 6 7 8 9 10 11 12 13 14 15 16 17 18 19 20

Check-up 3 Number

3

1 Write the missing numbers.

15 | 16 | 17 | 18 | 19 | 20

2 Write the missing numbers.

12 | 13 | 14 | 15 | 16 | 17

3 Write the answers.

1 less   **1** more   **10** less   **10** more

   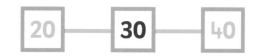

15 — 16 — 17   20 — 30 — 40

4 Count on from the larger number to find the answer.

$3 + 5 =$ 8

5 Write the answers.

$4 + 1 =$ 5 $5 - 3 =$ 2

6 Write the answers.

$7 + 7 =$ 14   6 $+ 4 = 10$

7 Write the number that fits.

15 | 16 | 17

8 Write the answers.

$1 + 8 =$ 9 $9 - 4 =$ 5

9 Write the missing numbers.

| 6 | 8 | 10 | 12 | 14 |

| 0 | 5 | 10 | 15 | 20 |

| 0 | 10 | 20 | 30 | 40 |

10 Write the answers.

$2 + 2 + 2 =$ 6 $5 + 5 + 5 + 5 =$ 20 $10 + 10 =$ 20

11 Share the cakes equally. Write how many are on each plate.

3

12 Write the answer.

$15 - 6 =$ 9

13 Write the answers.

What is half of **8**? 4   What is a quarter of **8**? 2

0 1 2 3 4 5 6 7 8 9 10 11 12 13 14 15 16 17 18 19 20

Check-up 4 Shape and space, Measures, Handling data

1 How long is this ribbon?

☐☐☐☐☐☐ [6] squares

2 Draw the hands with the times under.

8 o'clock   Half past **4**

3 Draw the answer.

The path to the house is not finished.

Draw a path.

Make it turn to the right.

From: **First Mental Arithmetic 3 Answers** by Ann Montague-Smith (ISBN 978 07217 1171 3). Copyright © Schofield & Sims Ltd, 2011. Published by Schofield & Sims Ltd, Dogley Mill, Fenay Bridge, Huddersfield HD8 0NQ, UK (www.schofieldandsims.co.uk). This page may be photocopied for use within your school or institution only.

4 This is half of a butterfly. Finish the picture.

5 Draw a line to show half.

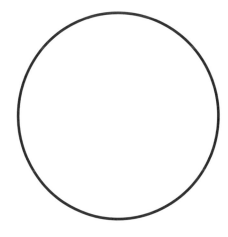

6 Draw 2 lines to show a quarter.

   or

From: **First Mental Arithmetic 3 Answers** by Ann Montague-Smith (ISBN 978 07217 1171 3). Copyright © Schofield & Sims Ltd, 2011. Published by Schofield & Sims Ltd,
Dogley Mill, Fenay Bridge, Huddersfield HD8 0NQ, UK (www.schofieldandsims.co.uk). This page may be photocopied for use within your school or institution only.

7 Draw the shapes where they fit on the Carroll diagram.

Has straight lines	Does not have straight lines

8 Draw a line as long as these bricks.

9 Draw a shape with 3 straight sides.

From: **First Mental Arithmetic 3 Answers** by Ann Montague-Smith (ISBN 978 07217 1171 3). Copyright © Schofield & Sims Ltd, 2011. Published by Schofield & Sims Ltd, Dogley Mill, Fenay Bridge, Huddersfield HD8 0NQ, UK (www.schofieldandsims.co.uk). This page may be photocopied for use within your school or institution only.

Check-up 4
Shape and space, Measures, Handling data

Session Focus
Length
Telling the time to the hour and half hour
Turning
Symmetry
Halves and quarters
Carroll diagrams
Shape

4

1 How long is this ribbon?

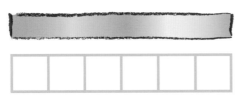

6 squares

2 Draw the hands with the times under.

8 o'clock   Half past 4

3 Draw the answer.

The path to the house is not finished.

Draw a path.

Make it turn to the right.

4 This is half of a butterfly. Finish the picture.

5 Draw a line to show half.

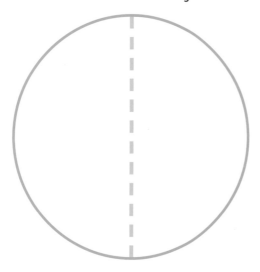

6 Draw 2 lines to show a quarter.

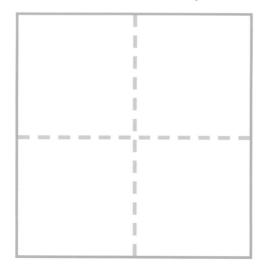   or

7 Draw the shapes where they fit on the Carroll diagram.

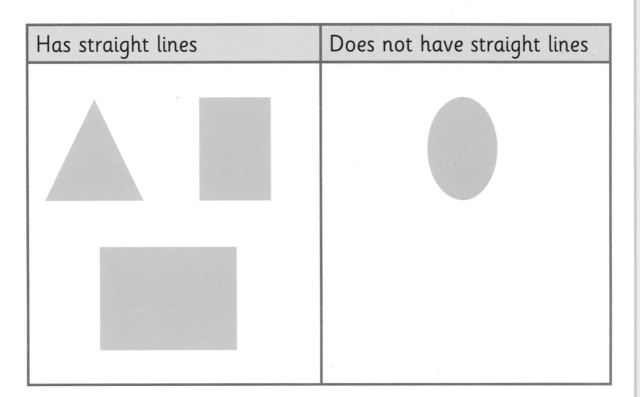

Has straight lines	Does not have straight lines

8 Draw a line as long as these bricks.

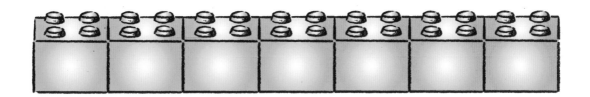

9 Draw a shape with 3 straight sides.

Section 1 Group record sheet

Class _____

Name	Read and write numerals to 20	Put numbers onto a number track or line	Compare and order numbers	Write 1/10 more/less numbers	Add by counting on	Subtract as difference	Subtract one-digit from a two-digit number	Totals of 10	Add and subtract to 5	Doubles of all numbers to 10	Symmetry	Carroll diagrams
	Session 1	Session 1	Session 1	Session 2	Session 2	Session 2	Session 3	Session 3	Session 4	Session 4	Session 5	Session 5

From: **First Mental Arithmetic 3 Answers** by Ann Montague-Smith (ISBN 978 07217 1171 3). Copyright © Schofield & Sims Ltd, 2011. Published by Schofield & Sims Ltd, Dogley Mill, Fenay Bridge, Huddersfield HD8 0NQ, UK (www.schofieldandsims.co.uk). This page may be photocopied for use within your school or institution only.

Section 2   Group record sheet

Class _____

Name	Measure length	Doubles of numbers to 10	Add and subtract	Count in 1s, 2s, 5s, and 10s	Combine groups of 2, 5 or 10	Share into equal groups	Time to the hour and half hour	Subtraction of one-digit from a two-digit number	Position, direction, and movement	Turning	Halves and quarters
	Session 1	Session 1	Session 1	Session 2	Session 2	Session 2	Session 3	Session 3	Session 4	Session 5	Session 5

From: **First Mental Arithmetic 3 Answers** by Ann Montague-Smith (ISBN 978 07217 1171 3). Copyright © Schofield & Sims Ltd, 2011. Published by Schofield & Sims Ltd, Dogley Mill, Fenay Bridge, Huddersfield HD8 0NQ, UK (www.schofieldandsims.co.uk). This page may be photocopied for use within your school or institution only.

Full list of the Schofield & Sims First Mental Arithmetic books

Workbooks

First Mental Arithmetic 1	ISBN 978 07217 1163 8
First Mental Arithmetic 2	ISBN 978 07217 1164 5
First Mental Arithmetic 3	ISBN 978 07217 1165 2
First Mental Arithmetic 4	ISBN 978 07217 1166 9
First Mental Arithmetic 5	ISBN 978 07217 1167 6
First Mental Arithmetic 6	ISBN 978 07217 1168 3

Answers

First Mental Arithmetic 1 Answers	ISBN 978 07217 1169 0
First Mental Arithmetic 2 Answers	ISBN 978 07217 1170 6
First Mental Arithmetic 3 Answers	ISBN 978 07217 1171 3
First Mental Arithmetic 4 Answers	ISBN 978 07217 1172 0
First Mental Arithmetic 5 Answers	ISBN 978 07217 1173 7
First Mental Arithmetic 6 Answers	ISBN 978 07217 1174 4

Related materials

The **I can do** teaching method was devised for use at Key Stage 2, with **Schofield & Sims Mental Arithmetic**, and has achieved outstanding results.

This teaching method is equally suitable for use at Key Stage 1, with **First Mental Arithmetic**.

To find out more, watch the film **'I can do maths' in practice** online at **www.schofieldandsims.co.uk/icando/** and order the **I can do maths** Teacher's Guide.

I can do maths Teacher's Guide	ISBN 978 07217 1115 7

All available from

Schofield & Sims Ltd, Dogley Mill, Fenay Bridge, Huddersfield HD8 0NQ

www.schofieldandsims.co.uk

E-mail: sales@schofieldandsims.co.uk
Phone: 01484 607080 Facsimile: 01484 606815